MAL

County Council

Libraries, books and more...........

Please return/renew this item by the last date shown.
Library items may also be renewed by phone on
030 33 33 1234 (24hours) or via our website

www.cumbria.gov.uk/libraries

Cumbria Libraries
CLIC
Interactive Catalogue
Ask for a CLIC password

LONDON·SYDNEY

Franklin Watts
First published in Great Britain in 2018
by The Watts Publishing Group

Text © Steve Barlow and Steve Skidmore 2018
Illustrations © The Watts Publishing Group 2018
Illustrator: Lee Robinson
Cover design: Peter Scoulding
Executive Editor: Adrian Cole

ISBN 978 1 4451 5918 8
ebook ISBN 978 1 4451 5919 5
Library ebook ISBN 978 1 4451 5920 1

1 3 5 7 9 10 8 6 4 2

Printed and bound by CPI Group (UK) Ltd, Croydon, CR0 4YY

Franklin Watts
An imprint of
Hachette Children's Group
Part of The Watts Publishing Group
Carmelite House
50 Victoria Embankment
London EC4Y 0DZ

An Hachette UK Company
www.hachette.co.uk

www.franklinwatts.co.uk

HOW TO BE A HERO

With most books, you read from the beginning to the end and then stop. You can then read it backwards if you like, but that would be silly.

But in this book, you're the hero. That's why it's called *I Hero*, see?

You read a bit, then you make a choice that takes you to a different part of the book. You might jump from Section 3 to Section 47 or Section 28. Crazy, huh?

If you make a good choice, **GREAT!**

BUUUUUUT...

If you make the wrong choice, **ALL KINDS OF BAD STUFF WILL HAPPEN.**

Hah-ha! Loser! You'll have to start again.

But that won't happen to you, will it?
Because you're not a zero — **YOU'RE A HERO!**

You are a kitten living in a tough, rough part of the city.

The streets are ruled by the Ugly Pug gang. They take what they want, when they want and don't let anyone get in their way.

The pugs rule by fear.

You and the other cats and creatures of the city have never stood up to them. But maybe it's about time that someone did...

Go to 1.

1

You are walking along the street minding your own business. Turning a corner, you see a group of Ugly Pug gang members robbing an old female, ginger cat.

She sees you and cries out, "Help me!"

If you want to help, go to 24.
If you want to ignore her, go to 28.

2

"Of course I am!" you say. "I can block out pain!"

Master Yeeha raises an eyebrow. "Very well, if you think that, then you must seek them out."

You head into the city. Before very long you see a group of Ugly Pugs hanging around the street corner.

"Oi, ugly mugs," you say. "You've got my locket and I want it back!"

They laugh. "And how are you going to get it back?"

If you wish to fight them, go to 13.

If you want to talk to them, go to 43.

3

You race to the museum entrance and come to a sudden stop. There's a long queue to get in and you don't have time to lose. *Never mind,* you think, *I'll climb over the wall.*

You race up the wall, leap up and over it...

...and get arrested by security.

Uh oh!

You need to spend some thinking time in a cramped jail cell.

GO BACK TO 1.

4

"Thanks, but no thanks." You pick yourself up off the floor. "The way of this kitten is to go home and have a nice saucer of milk."

The old cat shakes his head. "Do you always want to live in fear, always be looking over your shoulder, always be thinking what could have been?"

You consider for a moment. Maybe the old cat could help...

Go to 30.

You shake your head. "What move did you use on me? It was so fast I couldn't see it."

Master Yeeha looks serious. "I used the ultimate move of the Way of the Kitten. I used the Cat of Nine Tails. Here, I'll show you in slow motion," Master Yeeha said, leaping into the air.

"You spin around and hit your opponent eight times with your tail. This takes away their strength. Then with the ninth spin, you hit their jaw with your tail... But it takes time to learn. Is this something you want to do?"

You think of the Ugly Pugs out there in the city and of your stolen locket. Do you have the time to learn this move?

To learn the Cat of Nine Tails, go to 14.
If you think you should take on the Ugly Pugs immediately, go to 31.

6

The Ugly Pug swings you around his head several times before letting go.

"WHAAAHHH!" You find yourself flying through the air...

SPLAT!

You land head first into a waste bin. The smell is disgusting! You gag and cough up a furball. Rotting food and even worse things that you don't want to think about, stick to your fur.

If you want to get out of the bin immediately, go to 10.

If you decide to wait for the Ugly Pugs to leave, go to 47.

7

"Surely you should teach me how to block out the pain before I do that?" you say.

Master Yeeha smiles. "You are correct. Well done. You have remembered the second lesson of the Way of the Kitten. I will now show you how to become a master of your mind!"

Go to 49.

"I'm very sorry," you say. You lick at your fur. "Nice ice cream, though."

The shopkeeper isn't amused. "How are you going to pay for that?"

At that moment a few coins land on the counter. "Don't worry, we'll sort the ice cat out…"

You spin around and gasp in horror. It's the Ugly Pugs!

"It looks like you're the cat who got the cream. Ice cream, that is," says the leader. He waves at the shopkeeper. "Have an ice day…" He jabs a paw into your face. "Unlike yours, which is going to be CATastrophic."

The Ugly Pugs guffaw, grab hold of you and march you outside.

Go to 48.

9

"Meeeeeeowwwww!" You attack using the Double Claw move, but suddenly realise you've chosen the wrong move!

The Ugly Pugs easily beat off your attack! They move in, growling…

Go to 29.

10

You leap out of the bin and try to brush the gunk off your fur. The Ugly Pugs see you and in the blink of an eye, they are standing over you.

"Going somewhere?" the very ugly one asks.

"Er no..." you stammer.

"Well get back into the bin."

You shrug obediently and climb back into the bin. The Ugly Pugs empty another waste bin onto your head. Again, you gag and cough up a furball. This is not a good day!

If you want to stay in the bin, go to 47.

If you want to fight the Ugly Pugs, go to 13.

11

"No way," you reply. "I believe that I will drown if I jump into the river."

Instead of being angry with you, Master Yeeha cheers. "Wonderful! By standing up to me, you believed in yourself. You also learnt the second lesson of the Way of the Kitten."

"Did I? What's that?" you ask.

"Never listen to anyone who asks you to do something stupid! Your training has started well! Meet me here tomorrow and we will continue..."

Aren't you the clever cat! Go to 23.

Master Yeeha teaches you the Double Claw.
"Use this when you are in a restricted space,"
he says.

You practise the move.

Maser Yeeha nods. "Good. Now it is your
turn to attack me using it," he says.

You leap at the old Siamese cat.

THUMP!

You are thrown against the wall. You slither
down it. Master Yeeha laughs...

**If you have learnt the Flying Kitten move,
go to 5.**

If you haven't, go to 36.

13

You clench your fists. "Come on! Let's see what you've got..."

Seconds later you realise that the Ugly Pugs have got a lot. You lie on the floor battered and bruised, knowing that you don't have the fighting skills to stand up to the Ugly Pugs.

Too late you remember the old saying — "Those who fight and run away, don't get birds flying round their head today."

What were you thinking of? GO BACK TO 1. **Next time, don't be so dumb!**

14

You think carefully before bowing to Master Yeeha. "I would be honoured if you taught me the Cat of Nine Tails."

Master Yeeha smiles. "I will!"

Go to 26.

15

You launch yourself at Slackface

"MEEOO – OH NO!"

As you head towards him, Slackface picks up a trash can, holds it out and you fly straight into it! **CLANG!**

He slams the lid shut. You're trapped!

Go to 22.

16

You stop and look up at the old Siamese. "Are you talking to me?" you ask.

"Here, no one else is." He replies.

"Why are you talking like that?" you ask.

The old cat coughs. "Er... Sorry, I saw someone do it in a film. I thought it makes me sound wise."

"No, it makes you sound weird," you reply.

"Well, never mind. I see that you are troubled. What has caused this?"

You tell him about the Ugly Pugs and losing your locket. The old cat listens to your story. "I can help you to recover this locket. I can teach you ways to defeat these bullies."

You laugh! **REALLY?** you think. **THIS OLD HAS-BEEN?**

If you think he can help you, go to 42.

If you want to ignore him, go to 20.

17

"You are the master, so it is best that you make the choice," you say.

"You have chosen well," smiles Master Yeeha. "You have now learnt the third lesson of the Way of the Kitten — allow your master to show you the way. You can only begin to learn kung fu fighting moves when your mind is strong and can overcome anything."

He takes you to a fire pit of hot coals. "Pain is only an illusion. This is a test of mind over matter. Walk across the fire."

If you want to obey Master Yeeha, go to 45.

If you don't want to, go to 7.

18

You run into the ice-cream shop and slip on an ice cream that a kid has just dropped.

"WHAAAHHH!" You go flying into the air and land smack in the middle of the ice-cream counter. You are covered in chocolate chip and raspberry ripple ice cream! The shopkeeper isn't impressed. "I'm not impressed," she says.

If you wish to apologise to her, go to 8.

If you think you should get out of there RIGHT NOW, go to 34.

19

Ignoring her pleas, you hurry past the old cat. As you turn the corner, you bump into Master Yeeha.

He looks angry. "Walking away from a cat in distress is cowardly. This is NOT the Way of the Kitten. Begone! You are not worthy of my teaching!"

You deserve all you get, you cowardly cat! GO BACK TO 1.

20

That's all I need, you think, *a crazy old cat...* "Thanks, but no thanks," you say and turn away. Ignoring the old Siamese cat's pleas to listen to him, you carry on down the street.

Just before you arrive back home, you tell yourself to go and listen to what the old cat had to say. After all, what harm is there in that?

You hurry back to the wall, but he is gone. You'll never know what help you might have received.

GO BACK TO 1, AND BEGIN YOUR ADVENTURE AGAIN.

"So long, suckers!" you cry, sprinting up the road and laughing at the Ugly Pugs.

SPLAT!

Sadly, you get mown down by a herd of elderly zebras on mobility scooters.

Oops, you didn't see that coming! You're a flat cat! GO BACK TO 1.

22

You feel the trash can being picked up. You try and break free, but you can't.

Seconds later you feel yourself flying through the air.

SPLASH!

You've been thrown into the river!

GLUG...

...GLUG...

...GLUG!

Slackface has proved to be top dog! GO BACK TO 1.

23

Next day, Master Yeeha takes you to his kung fu temple.

"Which move would you like to learn first?" he asks. *The Double Claw* or the *Flying Kitten*?"

If you want to learn the Double Claw move, go to 35.

To learn the Flying Kitten move, go to 27.

If you want Master Yeeha to decide, go to 17.

"Leave her alone!" you bravely shout at the Ugly Pugs.

They turn and laugh. "Okay, okay," says the ugliest Ugly Pug. "We'll do as you say. We'll leave her alone." They let go of the old cat, who runs off.

The leader smiles. "But as for you..." The Ugly Pugs charge at you. You nearly wet yourself!

If you want to stand up to the Ugly Pugs, go to 13.

If you want to run away, go to 44.

You stare at the Ugly Pug. "No way," you say.

The Ugly Pug laughs. "What a little, witty kitty! Now stop joking and give me the locket."

The other Ugly Pugs move towards you, snarling.

If you decide to give up the locket, go to 32.

If you want to run away, go to 37.

If you want to fight the Ugly Pugs, go to 13.

The training is tough, but however hard you try, you are unable to master the move.

"You must persevere," says Master Yeeha. "This is another lesson of the Way of the Kitten."

Days pass and Master Yeeha teaches you more moves: the Spitting Furball, the Purrfect Paw, the Fist of the Feline and the Kicking Kitty, but you are still unable to master the Cat of Nine Tails.

One morning, you are making your way to another training session, when you see several Ugly Pugs picking on an old cat. You recognise her. It is the ginger cat you helped out many months ago!

She sees you and cries out, "Help me, please..."

If you want to fight the Ugly Pugs, go to 38.

If you decide to ignore her, go to 19.

27

"Let's start with the Flying Kitten," you say.

"As you wish!" Before you can blink, Master Yeeha picks you up, spins you around his head and throws you at the wall.

THUMP! SPLAT!

You lie battered and bruised on the floor. "Why did you do that?" you whimper.

"Your choice was not wise," replies Master Yeeha.

Go to 17.

28

This is nothing to do with me, you think. Head down, you turn and start to cross the road.

SPLUT!

Shame you didn't see the herd of jogging hippos coming your way.

You got what you deserved, you scaredy-cat! GO BACK TO 1.

You are in the open, so the Flying Kitten
is the purrfect move...

You launch yourself at the Ugly Pugs...

"Meeeeeowwwww!"

Seconds later the Ugly Pugs are lying on the ground, bruised and groaning. You stand over them. "Where's my locket?"

A deep voice sounds out. "I've got it!"

You turn around. It's the leader of the Ugly Pugs — Slackface!

If you want to ask Slackface to give you the locket, go to 33.

If you want to attack with the Double Claw move, go to 46.

To use the Flying Kitten move, go to 15.

30

"Okay, Master Yeeha," you say. "What do I have to do?"

"We will begin your training straight away," he replies. "Follow me."

Master Yeeha leads you to a high bridge that crosses a wide, deep river. "Jump from this bridge down into the river," he says.

"But I can't swim," you reply.

Master Yeeha shakes his head. "You must believe in yourself. This is the first lesson of the Way of the Kitten."

If you want to obey Master Yeeha, go to 39.

If you don't want to, go to 11.

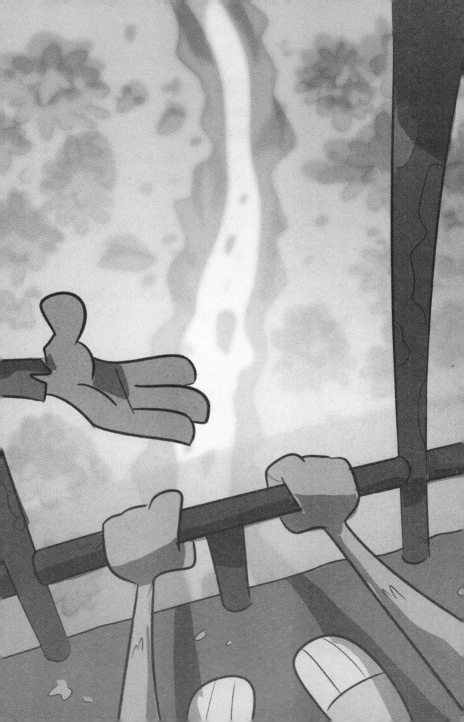

31

"The Ugly Pugs have been bullies for far too long and I want my locket back NOW!" you exclaim. "Their time is up. They are going to feel the power of the Way of the Kitten."

"Nice speech," says Master Yeeha, "but you are wrong. The Ugly Pugs will cause you much pain! Are you sure you want to do this?"

If you are, go to 2.

If you want to learn the Cat of Nine Tails move, go to 14.

32

Your knees shake as you hand over the locket.

The Ugly Pug takes it. "Thanks." He smiles and grabs hold of your tail. In an instant, you find yourself hanging upside down, looking into the Ugly Pug's ugly mug.

"We'd like to stay and chat, but we must fly," he laughs. "Or rather you must!"

Go to 6.

33

"I'm in a good mood today," you say, "so I'm going to give you the chance to give me the locket and get out of here..."

Slackface laughs. "And I'm in a good mood too, so I'm only going to hurt you a little bit!" He picks up a trash can and before you react, he throws you inside and slams the lid shut. You're trapped!

Why did you waste time talking to him? Go to 22.

34

You run out of the shop, but your ice-cream coat quickly attracts a swarm of wasps!

ARGHHHH!

You try to beat them off as they attack. You are covered in stings, but things suddenly get worse. You see the Ugly Pugs heading towards you!

To go to the museum to try to hide, go to 3.

To stand up and fight the Ugly Pugs, go to 13.

35

"Let's start with the Double Claw," you say.

"As you wish!" Before you can blink, Master Yeeha attacks you with his claws, hitting your face, left, right, left, right.

OW! ARRGHHH!

OUCH!

"What did you do that for?" you whimper.

"Your choice was not wise," replies Master Yeeha.

Go to 17.

Master Yeeha teaches you the Flying Kitten. "Use this move when you have time and space to attack," he says.

You practise the move.

Master Yeeha nods. "Good. Now attack me," he says.

You fly towards the old Siamese cat... who spins around and sends you flying into a huge brass gong...

DONG!

Your head is ringing, literally!

If you have already learnt the Double Claw move, go to 5.

If you haven't, go to 12.

37

You spin around, but before you can get away, the Ugly Pug grabs hold of your tail.

Suddenly you find yourself in the air, upside down and staring at the Ugly Pug's, ugly mug.

He snatches the locket from you. He laughs. "Thank you. And now, bye bye, it's time to fly!"

Go to 6.

38

"Hey, you ugly mugs, pick on someone your own size," you call out.

They turn around. "Oh, it's the scaredy-cat again," they laugh. "Are you ready for another Ugly Pug lesson?"

"I've learnt my lessons," you say. "And you're about to learn yours..."

If you want to use the Flying Kitten on the Ugly Pugs, go to 29.

To use the Double Claw, go to 9.

"Very well," you say. You climb to the bridge rail and jump. You plummet downwards out of control.

SPLOOSH!

Your head dips beneath the surface of the river. Desperately you try to keep afloat by catty paddling, but you know you are in trouble.

You hear Master Yeeha shouting, "You fool! Why did you do that?"

"You told me to," you reply.

"The second lesson of the Way of the Kitten, is not to listen to anyone who asks you to do something so stupid. You will never be a kung fu master. Goodbye!"

GLUG...
...GLUG...
...GLUG!

Start your adventure again! GO BACK TO 1.

"I have mastered mind over matter, Master Yeeha, but I have not yet learnt any kung fu fighting moves."

The old Siamese cat smiles. "But you have learnt another lesson in the Way of the Kitten. Don't pick a fight until you know you can win it. So, what moves should you learn? And this time, I will allow you to choose."

To learn the Flying Kitten, go to 36.

To learn the Double Claw, go to 12.

You begin to spin.

Once, twice...

You concentrate and time seems to slow down.

With every spin you hit Slackface with your tail.

Three, four...

You begin to speed up.

Five, six, seven, eight...

...Nine!

You hit Slackface square on his jaw with your tail. He looks at you in amazement and confusion. Then he falls to the floor in a crumpled heap.

You mastered the Cat of Nine Tails!
Go to 50.

42

"How can an old cat like you help me?" you ask.

Suddenly, the old cat leaps from the wall, picks you up and spins you around on one finger before slamming you to the ground.

He stands over you. "I am Master Yeeha and I can teach you to become a kung fu expert. You will learn... the Way of the Kitten!"

If you want to take up his offer, go to 30.

If you don't, go to 4.

43

One of the Ugly Pugs picks up a shovel and moves towards you.

You laugh. "You cannot hurt me. I have trained in the Way of the Kitten. I can overcome pain."

"Is that so? Let's see you overcome this..."

He hits you with the shovel.

CLANG!

You crumple to the ground as the Ugly Pugs walk off howling with laughter.

Maybe you should have learnt some good fight moves before you took on the uglies!
GO BACK TO 1.

You turn and run across the road, just ahead of a passing herd of jogging hippos.

That was lucky, you think. The Ugly Pugs can't get past the hippos. You have the chance to escape! Ahead of you is the entrance to the local museum and to your left is an ice-cream shop.

If you want to carry on running away, go to 21.

If you want to hide in the museum, go to 3.

If you want to head into the shop, go to 18.

You step onto the hot coals... **WHOOSH!**

OooowwWWW!

Your fur catches fire! You leap from the fire pit, blowing at your flaming hair.

"Did that hurt?" asks Master Yeeha.

"Of course it did!" you scream. "Mind over matter? What were you thinking of?"

"Well, I don't mind and you don't matter..." says Master Yeeha. "You forgot the second lesson of the Way of the Kitten. Never listen to anyone who asks you to do something stupid! Such a forgetful mind is no good to me. I cannot teach you. Goodbye!"

You're not such a hot shot! GO BACK TO 1.

46

"Meeooowwwww!" You launch into the Double Claw attack.

KAPOW! CRUNCH! POW!

But Slackface fights back! You try other

moves: the Purrfect Paw, the Spitting Furball, the Fist of the Feline, the Kicking Kitty, but Slackface counters every one of them.

"Is that all you've got?" he growls. "It's time to end this..."

You only have two moves left, and you haven't even mastered one of them!

To use the Flying Kitten move, go to 15.

To try the Cat of Nine Tails, go to 41.

You peer over the top of the bin and watch the Ugly Pugs heading away.

You pull yourself out of the bin and try to remove the worst of the stickiness from your fur.

Trudging down the street, you hear a voice from above.

"Sad you are. Something lost you have."

You look up to see an old Siamese cat sitting on a wall, staring at you. "Enough trouble you have had. Help you I can."

If you wish to ignore the old cat, go to 20.

If you wish to talk to him, go to 16.

48

The ugliest of the Ugly Pugs stoops down.
"You've caused us a lot of bother. You owe us."
He points at the silver locket hanging from
your collar. "Hand it over, now."

"But it was given to me by my mum," you
say.

"Well you can give it to us. Or else..."

**If you decide to give up the locket, go
to 32.**

**If you want to refuse to give up the locket,
go to 25.**

49

Over the next few weeks, Master Yeeha shows
you how to become a master of your mind.
Before long, you can walk over hot coals,
smash bricks in half with your paw and block
out pain.

After one training session, he calls you over.
"Are you ready to stand up to the Ugly Pugs?"
he asks.

If you think you are, go to 2.

If you don't think you are, go to 40.

"That's mine." You stand over Slackface and take back your locket. "You and your Ugly Pugs had better leave this city," you say.

He nods, and he and the Ugly Pugs crawl away, defeated as the townspeople gather around cheering. Master Yeeha steps out of the crowd. He smiles. "I saw everything. I have no more to teach you. You have learnt all the lessons of the Way of the Kitten. Take a bow, you are a true hero."

I HERO
TOONS
ATTACK of the ZOMBIE BUNNIES
Steve Barlow · Steve Skidmore
Illustrated by Lee Robinson
EDGE

You live in a small town. Your ma and pa grow vegetables for your rabbit friends and neighbours. So does everyone else you know.

Ma and Pa want you to help them run the farm, but you would rather invent stuff like an **AMAZING** super-fast-freeze ray gun.

You've come into town in the pick-up to help your ma and pa sell their crop at the market.

"Put that there gun contraption down!" grumbles Pa. "There ain't never gonna be no call for your dumb inventions!"

"But I thought we could **FREEZE** our vegetables..." you protest.

"Hogwash!" says Pa. "Help me stack these here carrots."

Go to 1.

Continue the adventure in:

About the 2Steves

"The 2Steves" are
Britain's most popular
writing double act
for young people,
specialising in comedy
and adventure. They
perform regularly in schools and libraries,
and at festivals, taking the power of words
and story to audiences of all ages.

Together they have written many books,
including the *I HERO Immortals* and *iHorror* series.

About the illustrator: Lee Robinson

Lee studied animation at Newcastle College and
went on to work on comics such as *Kung Fu
Panda* as well as running comicbook workshops
throughtout the northeast of England. When he's not
drawing, Lee loves running, reading and videogames.
He now lives in Edmonton, Canada, where's he's got
plenty of time to come up with crazy ideas while
waiting for the weather to warm up.

I HERO Legends — collect them all!

ATHENA

978 1 4451 5234 9 pb
978 1 4451 5235 6 ebook

BEOWULF

978 1 4451 5225 7 pb
978 1 4451 5226 4 ebook

KING ARTHUR

978 1 4451 5231 8 pb
978 1 4451 5232 5 ebook

FREYA

978 1 4451 5237 0 pb
978 1 4451 5238 7 ebook

HERCULES

978 1 4451 5228 8 pb
978 1 4451 5229 5 ebook

ROBIN HOOD

978 1 4451 5183 0 pb
978 1 4451 5184 7 ebook

Have you read the I HERO Atlantis Quest mini series?

MENACE FROM THE DEEP
Steve Barlow - Steve Skidmore

978 1 4451 2867 2 pb
978 1 4451 2868 9 ebook

OCEAN ALLIANCE
Steve Barlow - Steve Skidmore

978 1 4451 2870 2 pb
978 1 4451 2871 9 ebook

BATTLE FOR THE SEAS
Steve Barlow - Steve Skidmore

978 1 4451 2876 4 pb
978 1 4451 2877 1 ebook

ATLANTIS ASSAULT
Steve Barlow - Steve Skidmore

978 1 4451 2873 3 pb
978 1 4451 2874 0 ebook

Also by the 2Steves...